PRAYER JOURNAL
FOR THE

THE
dreamer + THE doer

Well done, my good and faithful servant. You have been
faithful in handling this small amount, so now I will give
you many more responsibilities.
Let's celebrate together!

Matthew 25:21 (NLT)

cover quote written by Jenn Sprinkle

———DOWNLOAD———

*brain dump all of
the thoughts that
are distracting you
before you pray*

———PRAISE———

*jot down praise,
thanks and
answered prayers-
don't forget to
date them*

———LOVE———

*who do you need to
make amends with
or send a written
letter to?*

*who has the Lord
laid on your heart
to love on*

———DREAM———

*record
creative ideas and
dreams birthed*

———DO———

*now go do well....
not perfectly,
but {well}
what are your
action items this
week...or month?*

———{well}———

The Dreamer & The Doer Journal
Copyright © 2014 by
Jenn Sprinkle and Kelly Rucker
of The {well} Studio

All rights reserved.

Published by:
NyreePress Literary Group
P.O. Box 164882
Fort Worth, TX 76161
www.nyreepress.com

"She Chooses Grace" written by Jenn Sprinkle

ISBN print: 978-0-9909652-7-5
Library of Congress Control Number: 2014957424

Christian Living / Inspirational / Prayer

Printed in the United States of America

DOWNLOAD

PRAISE

LOVE

DREAM

DO

{well}

DOWNLOAD

PRAISE

LOVE

DREAM

DO

{well}

DOWNLOAD

PRAISE

LOVE

DREAM

DO

{well}

DOWNLOAD

PRAISE

LOVE

DREAM

DO

{well}

DOWNLOAD

PRAISE

LOVE

DREAM

DO

{well}

DOWNLOAD

PRAISE

LOVE

DREAM

DO

{well}

DOWNLOAD

PRAISE

LOVE

DREAM

DO

{well}

DOWNLOAD

PRAISE

LOVE

DREAM

DO

{well}

DOWNLOAD

PRAISE

LOVE

DREAM

DO

{well}

DOWNLOAD

PRAISE

LOVE

DREAM

DO

{well}

DOWNLOAD

PRAISE

LOVE

DREAM

DO

{well}

DOWNLOAD

PRAISE

LOVE

DREAM

DO

{well}

DOWNLOAD

PRAISE

LOVE

DREAM

DO

{well}

DOWNLOAD

PRAISE

LOVE

DREAM

DO

{well}

DOWNLOAD

PRAISE

LOVE

DREAM

DO

{well}

DOWNLOAD

PRAISE

LOVE

DREAM

DO

{well}

DOWNLOAD

PRAISE

LOVE

DREAM

DO

{well}

DOWNLOAD

PRAISE

LOVE

DREAM

DO

{well}

DOWNLOAD

PRAISE

LOVE

DREAM

DO

{well}

DOWNLOAD

PRAISE

LOVE

DREAM

DO

{well}

DOWNLOAD

PRAISE

LOVE

DREAM

DO

{well}

DOWNLOAD

PRAISE

LOVE

DREAM

DO

{well}

DOWNLOAD

PRAISE

LOVE

DREAM

DO

{well}

DOWNLOAD

PRAISE

LOVE

DREAM

DO

{well}

DOWNLOAD

PRAISE

LOVE

DREAM

DO

{well}

DOWNLOAD

PRAISE

LOVE

DREAM

DO

{well}

DOWNLOAD

PRAISE

LOVE

DREAM

DO

{well}

DOWNLOAD

PRAISE

LOVE

DREAM

DO

{well}

DOWNLOAD

PRAISE

LOVE

DREAM

DO

{well}

DOWNLOAD

PRAISE

LOVE

DREAM

DO

{well}

DOWNLOAD

PRAISE

LOVE

DREAM

DO

{well}

DOWNLOAD

PRAISE

LOVE

DREAM

DO

{well}

DOWNLOAD

PRAISE

LOVE

DREAM

DO

{well}

DOWNLOAD

PRAISE

LOVE

DREAM

DO

{well}

DOWNLOAD

PRAISE

LOVE

DREAM

DO

{well}

DOWNLOAD

PRAISE

LOVE

DREAM

DO

{well}

DOWNLOAD

PRAISE

LOVE

DREAM

DO

{well}

DOWNLOAD

PRAISE

LOVE

DREAM

DO

{well}

DOWNLOAD

PRAISE

LOVE

DREAM

DO

{well}

DOWNLOAD

PRAISE

LOVE

DREAM

DO

{well}

PRAISE

LOVE

DREAM

DO

{well}

DOWNLOAD

PRAISE

LOVE

DREAM

DO

{well}

PRAISE

LOVE

DREAM

DO

{well}

DOWNLOAD

PRAISE

LOVE

DREAM

DO

{well}

CPSIA information can be obtained
at www.ICGtesting.com
Printed in the USA
LVRC010821020419
612642LV00001BA/55